What next, Charlie Brown?

by Charles M. Schulz

Selected Cartoons from
YOU'RE OUT OF YOUR MIND, CHARLIE BROWN!

Vol. II

A Crest Reprint

Fawcett Publications, Inc., Greenwich, Conn.
Member of American Book Publishers Council, Inc.

This book, prepared especially for Fawcett Publications, Inc., comprises the second half of YOU'RE OUT OF YOUR MIND, CHARLIE BROWN!, and is published by arrangement with Holt, Rinehart and Winston, Inc.

PRINTING HISTORY

First Holt, Rinehart and Winston printing, February 1959
Ninth printing, April 1964

First Crest printing, June 1965

Crest Books are published by Fawcett World Library,
67 West 44th Street, New York, N. Y. 10036.
Printed in the United States of America.

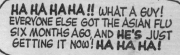

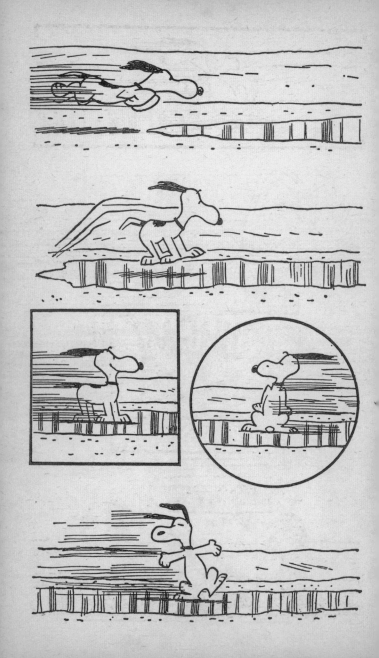

SCHROEDER, I'VE BEEN THINKING...

WHAT IF YOU AND I WERE TO GET MARRIED SOMEDAY, AND HAVE A LOT OF CHILDREN?

RUN, CHARLIE BROWN! GET IT UP! GET IT UP! RUN FASTER!! RUN! RUN!

I CAN'T STAND IT!

YOU SHOULD'A' SLUGGED HER, CHARLIE BROWN! EVEN IF SHE IS MY SISTER, I SAY YOU SHOULD HAVE SLUGGED HER!

YOU DON'T UNDERSTAND, LINUS... CHARLIE BROWN DID A VERY ADMIRABLE THING.. HE WOULD NEVER THINK OF HITTING A GIRL, SO HE DELIBERATELY HUMILIATED HIMSELF TO HOLD ON TO HIS HIGH MORAL STANDARDS!

ISN'T THAT RIGHT, CHARLIE BROWN?

NO, I WAS JUST AFRAID OF GETTING BEAT UP!

SCHULZ

MY MOTHER DIDN'T RAISE ME TO SPEND MY WHOLE LIFE CHASING STICKS!

CLOMP!

MAY I HELP YOU WITH YOUR PUZZLE, LUCY?

NO! BESIDES, I'M ALMOST DONE..

PLEASE?

OH, GOOD GRIEF! ALL RIGHT! HERE...YOU CAN PUT IN THE LAST PIECE..

CHARGE!

HEY! WHAT'RE Y'DOING THERE?!! WHAT'RE Y'DOING WITH THOSE PLIERS? HEY!

CLOMP!

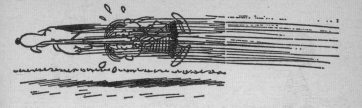

YOU DRIVE ME CRAZY!

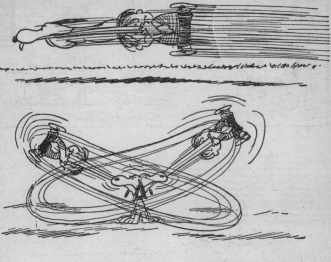

AND **THERE** HE **GOES!**

WHOOSH!

I'M THE FIRST DOG EVER TO LAUNCH A HUMAN BEING!

SOMETIMES HE WRITES, SOMETIMES HE DRAWS, SOMETIMES HE JUST SKETCHES...

·EVERY NOW AND THEN HE LIKES TO DO A **MURAL**!

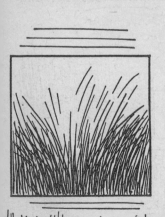

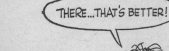

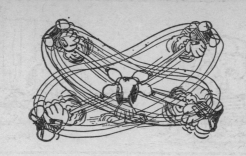

NO MANAGER IN THE HISTORY OF BASEBALL HAS EVER HAD TO GO THROUGH WHAT I HAVE TO GO THROUGH!

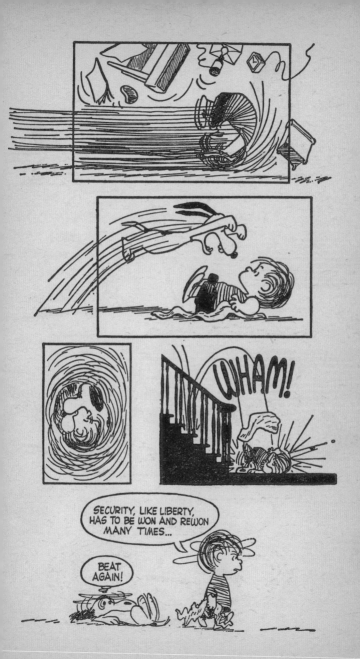